This Annual belongs to

Princess...

(Write your name here)

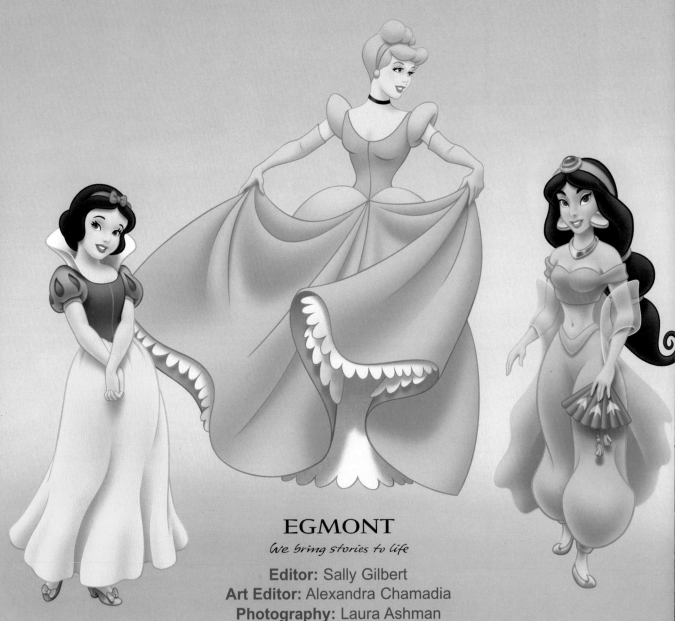

EGMONT

We bring stories to life

Editor: Sally Gilbert
Art Editor: Alexandra Chamadia
Photography: Laura Ashman

First published in Great Britain in 2006 by Egmont UK Limited,
239 Kensington High Street, London W8 6SA.

Note to parents: adult supervision is recommended when sharp-pointed items such as scissors are in use.

Disney's Princess

Annual 2007

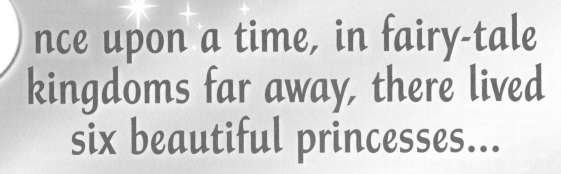

Once upon a time, in fairy-tale kingdoms far away, there lived six beautiful princesses...

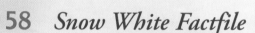

Turn the page to begin the fairy tale ...

Ariel Factfile

Personality:
Ariel is adventurous,
brave and fun-loving

Appearance:
Lovely red hair and
sparkling blue eyes

Romance:
Prince Eric

Family:
Her father, King Triton,
and her beautiful sisters

All About Me

Complete this fill-in, all about yourself.

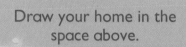

Draw your home in the space above.

My Factfile

Her Royal Highness Princess:
(Write your name below.)

....

Address of Royal residence:

....

....

....

Telephone:

....

Age:

....

Birthday:

....

9

Jewels for a Princess

1 One day, Ariel and Flounder were swimming through the Underwater Kingdom, looking for things to make into jewellery.

2 Ariel found some shells that were perfect for a necklace. But her sisters all laughed when they saw the necklace.

3 "I'll show them!" said Ariel. She decided to visit the Forbidden Kingdom for new ideas. Little did she know that Ursula was watching.

4 Soon, Ariel met some whales. "Can you help me make my jewellery?" she asked them. "Try the seahorses!" the whales replied, with a smile.

5 Ariel thanked the whales and followed their directions to find the seahorses. Deeper and deeper she swam ...

6 ... until, at last, she arrived in a huge cavern, filled with treasure. It was the seahorses' den.

7 The seahorses were really friendly. When Ariel told them why she was there, they were only too glad to help.

8 The seahorses showed Ariel some jewellery they had made themselves. "Take anything you want as our gift to you!" they told her.

9 Ariel thanked the seahorses and said goodbye. But on her way home, Ursula tried to snatch Ariel's new jewellery from her.

10 Luckily, King Triton appeared and trapped Ursula. "Your sisters have been looking for you," he told Ariel. "You'd better go and see them!"

11 Ariel's sisters were impressed with her jewellery. "You always look good," they told Ariel. "But now you look better than ever!"

The End

12

Use the little picture in the small frame
to help you colour in this page.

13

Sea-pearl Chest

Make this chest to store away all your treasures.

You will need:

tea box

dry rice

glue

jewels

paint

paintbrush

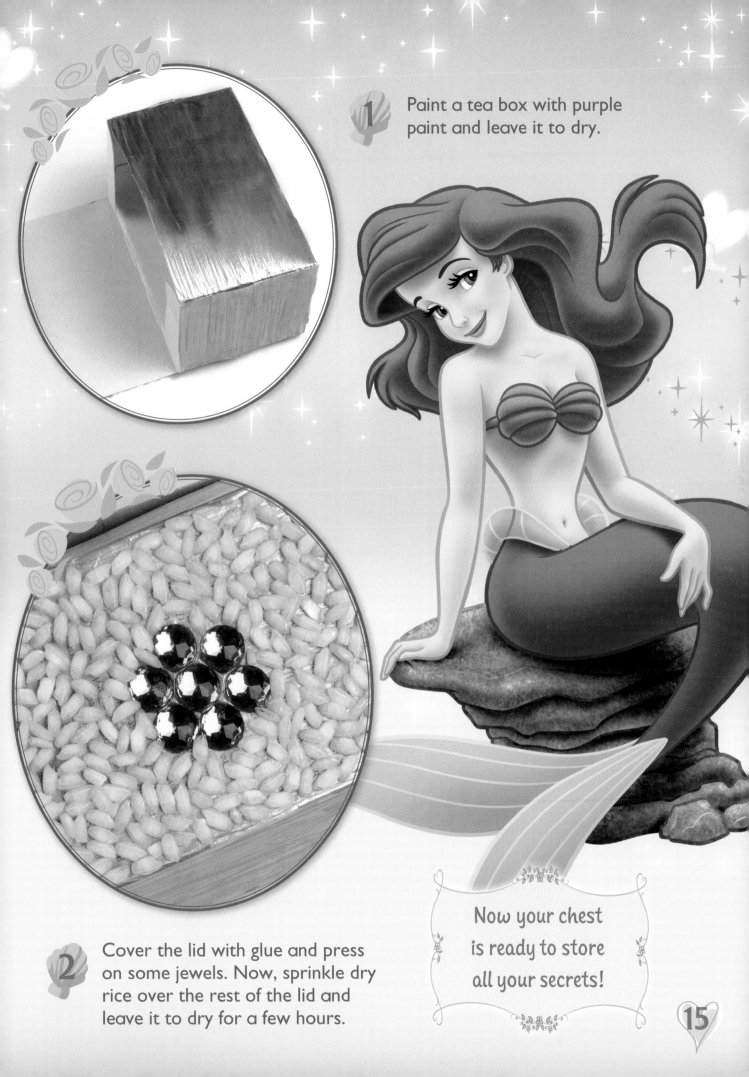

1 Paint a tea box with purple paint and leave it to dry.

2 Cover the lid with glue and press on some jewels. Now, sprinkle dry rice over the rest of the lid and leave it to dry for a few hours.

Now your chest is ready to store all your secrets!

15

Sea Sequences

Each line forms a pattern. Can you work out which object is missing each time?

Answers:
1 = sea-flower. 2 = oyster shell. 3 = seahorse. 4 Sebastian.

Fishy Fun

Ariel and Flounder are trying to complete this quiz.
Can you help them by circling the correct answers?

1 What is Ariel's royal father called?

a) King Trident
b) King Triton
c) King Terry

2 Where do Ariel and all her friends live?

a) Under the moon
b) Under the sun
c) Under the sea

3 What type of creature is Flounder?

a) A shark
b) A whale
c) A Guppy fish

Answer:
1 = b, 2 = c, 3 = c.

Cinderella Factfile

Personality:
Cinderella is strong, caring, kind and romantic

Appearance:
Blonde hair and blue eyes

Romance:
Prince Charming

Family:
Her father and stepfamily; Lady Tremaine, Anastasia and Drizella

Princess Looks

Complete this fill-in, all about how you look.

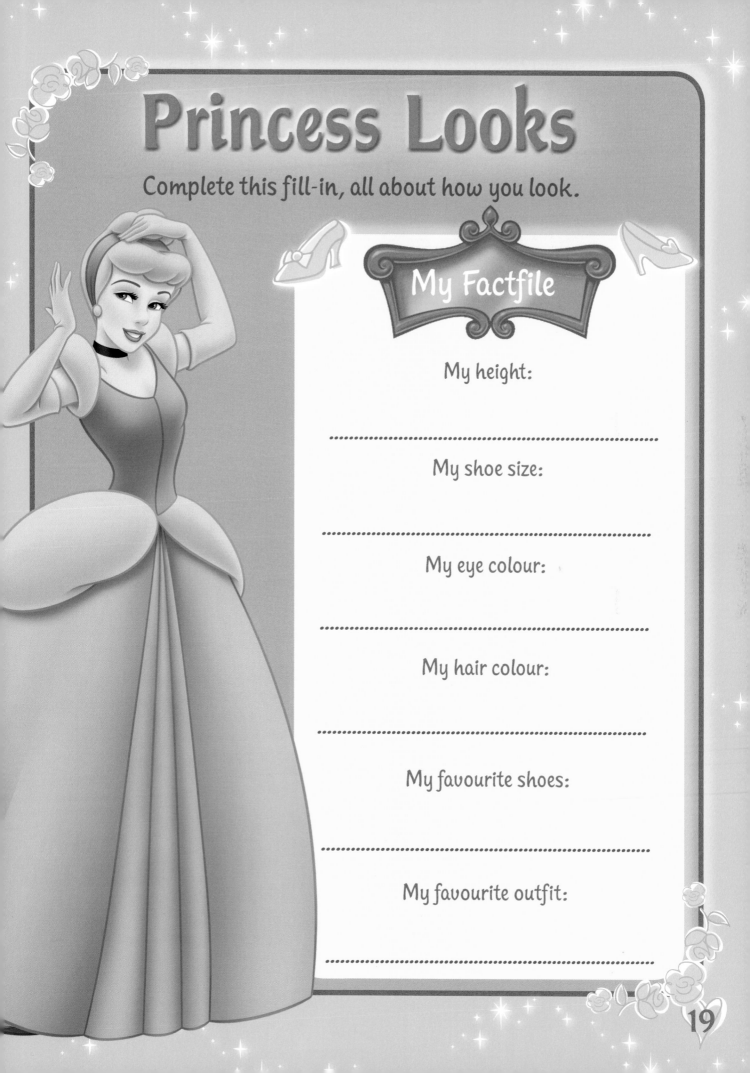

My Factfile

My height:

....

My shoe size:

....

My eye colour:

....

My hair colour:

....

My favourite shoes:

....

My favourite outfit:

....

Trouble with Lucifer

1 Cinderella and Prince Charming were having a party with the mice and the birds at the palace.

2 But, as usual, Lucifer started causing trouble by chasing the mice.

3 Cinderella asked Lucifer to go away and stop bothering them.

4 The mice thanked Cinderella. "But he'll only come back," Gus told her. "He always does," added Jaq.

5 Cinderella decided to do something about Lucifer, once and for all. She went to ask the Fairy Godmother for some help.

6 "Don't worry," the Fairy Godmother said. "I have an idea!"

7 Later, Lucifer reappeared and started chasing the mice again.

8 So the Fairy Godmother cast a spell that made Lucifer hate the sight of mice!

9 Lucifer hated mice so much that he climbed into an empty bird cage to get away from them! The stepsisters were very alarmed at Lucifer's behaviour and took him home.

10 Everyone thanked the Fairy Godmother for saving the mice from Lucifer.

11 To celebrate, the Fairy Godmother used her magic to make the party even more magical than it was before!

The End

Use the little picture in the pumpkin to
help you colour in this page.

23

Princess Crown

Create this pretty crown - it's fit for a princess!

You will need:

You will need:

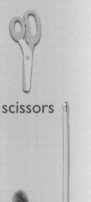

card

glue

scissors

pencil

feather trim

sticky tape

sequins

wrapping paper

1 Draw and cut out a crown shape from thick card

Note to parents: adult supervision is recommended when sharp-pointed items such as scissors are in use.

2 Decorate the crown with wrapping paper, a length of feather trim and jewels.

3 Finally, tape the crown into shape, so it fits your head. Now your crown is ready to wear!

25

Carriage Capers

Cinderella has been invited to a royal ball.

Can you spot the shadow that exactly matches Cinderella's carriage?

Answer:
Shadow b.

Test Your Memory

How much can you remember about our Cinderella story?
Try this quiz to find out!

 1 Who were Cinderella
and the Prince having
a party with?

a) The stepsisters
b) The mice and the birds
c) The King

 2 What were Gus
and Jaq afraid of?

a) Lucifer
b) The Fairy Godmother
c) The birds

 3 What happened at the end
of the story?

a) Everyone had a party
b) Cinderella went to sleep
c) The Prince left on business

Answers:
1 = b, 2 = a, 3 = a.

Jasmine Factfile

Personality: Fun, adventurous, exotic, determined and loyal

Romance: Aladdin

Appearance: Thick dark hair and brown eyes

Family: Her father, the Sultan of Agrabah

Princess Friends

Complete this fill-in, all about your very best friend.

Draw your friend in the space above.

My Friend

Name:

....

Address:

....

....

....

Age:

....

Telephone/mobile:

....

Birthday:

....

The Sweet Dress

1 There was to be a grand party at the palace, but Jasmine was having trouble choosing a dress to wear.

2 Just then, Aladdin arrived. "Let's take your mind off the party," he said. "Then I'm sure the perfect dress will come to you."

3 Aladdin took Jasmine on a magic-carpet ride. They were soon flying over a strange land, far away from the palace.

4 "I love these colourful fruits," said Jasmine, when they had landed on the island. "I definitely think my dress should be colourful."

5 Later, when they were flying home, Jasmine admired the stars in the sky. "I think my dress should be shiny, too!" she said.

6 Back at the palace, Jasmine went to see her father, who was scoffing sweets. It gave her a fantastic idea for the perfect dress!

7 "Sweet wrappers!" said Jasmine. "They are colourful, like fruit, and shiny, like stars!"

8 Jasmine set to work making herself a new dress. To give it some sparkle, she used the wrappers from the Sultan's sweets.

9 Later, it was time for the party. "You look wonderful," Aladdin told Jasmine, as they entered the ballroom.

10 "How did you get your dress so sparkly?" Aladdin asked, as they danced. "With the sweet things in life," said Jasmine. "Like you!"

The End

Use the little picture in the small frame
to help you colour in this page.

Star Brooch

Jasmine loves this star brooch, and so will you!

1 Cut out a shape like this one from card and decorate it with sequins.

Note to parents: adult supervision is recommended when sharp-pointed items are in use.

2 Glue a fabric star to the end of the card and leave it to dry.

3 Glue a brooch clasp to the back of the card, behind the star. Make a wish each time you wear your star brooch.

35

Jewellery Maze

Jasmine can't decide which accessory
to add to her outfit.

Can you follow the lines to see which one she chooses?

a

b

c

36

Answer:
Accessory b.

Magic Lamp Game

Help Jasmine collect four lamps before
you can make a wish!

How to play

This game is for two players. Find a similar-sized counter for each player. Take it in turns
to close your eyes and throw your counter on to this page. Each player has five goes at this.
The counter needs to land on any lamp at least four times for you to make a wish.
The counter should cover at least half of the lamp to count.

Belle Factfile

Personality:
Belle is kind, brave, loyal and determined

Romance:
The Beast

Appearance:
Belle is beautiful inside and out

Family:
Her father, Maurice

Birthday Princesses

Complete this fill-in, all about your friends' birthdays.

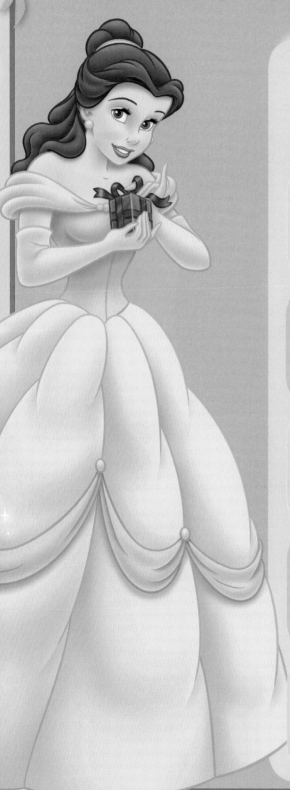

My Factfile

Name:...

Birthday:..

Name:...

Birthday:..

Name:...

Birthday:..

Name:...

Birthday:..

Name:...

Birthday:..

Belle's Wish

1 Belle was looking at some portraits of the Beast's ancestors. "How I would love to have met them all!" she said to herself.

2 Just then, a strange old lady knocked on the castle door.

3 The old lady offered Belle a beautiful golden egg. "This egg will grant you one wish!" she told Belle.

4 Belle bought the egg. "I wish I could have a party with the Beast's ancestors!" she said, holding it up.

5 But when Belle made her wish, nothing happened. She went to the library to find out what was wrong with the egg.

6 Meanwhile, the Beast found the egg and accidentally dropped it into the fire!

7 The Beast was very sorry. He promised Belle he would make it up to her.

8 The next morning, when Belle awoke, she saw lots of people in the garden. Belle assumed that they must have been invited by the Beast.

9 Belle rushed down to join their guests. "Why, it's all the Beast's ancestors!" cried Belle with joy.

10 Just then, the Beast appeared. "Thank you!" said Belle, happily. "It wasn't me," the Beast replied. "It must have been the egg, after all!"

11 Belle and the Beast danced until it got dark. "It was such fun meeting your ancestors," said Belle. "Now, I can see where you get your warm heart from!"

The End

42

Use the little picture in the garden urn
to help you colour in this page.

Crowning Glory

Follow these simple steps for this gorgeous Belle hairstyle.

1 Wash your hair with fragrant shampoo and leave it to dry.

2 Scoop the top half of your hair into a ponytail, and hold it in place with a hairband.

3

Add small plaits to the sides of your hair and secure with hairbands.

4

Add a rose hair accessory as a final princess touch.

Belle's Tip
Brush your hair until it shines!

45

Just Belle

See how much you know about Belle
with this quick quiz. Put a ✓ or x in the heart.

 1 This is
Clocksworth.

True 🤍 False 🤍

 2 Mrs Potts is
a teapot.

True 🤍 False 🤍

 3 This is Lumiere.

True 🤍 False 🤍

 4 The Enchanted
Rose is invisible.

True 🤍 False 🤍

Answers:
1 = False, it is Cogsworth, 2 = True,
3 = True, 4 = False, the Enchanted Rose
is not invisible.

Charming Changes

Belle and the Beast are joining their friends for a picnic.

These two pictures may look the same but there are 6 changes to the lower one. Can you spot them all?

47

Aurora Factfile

Personality:
Loving, romantic,
determined, kind and pure

Appearance:
Golden, wavy hair and
violet eyes

Romance:
Prince Phillip

Family:
King Stefan and the Queen

My Favourite Things

Complete this fill-in, all about your favourite things.

My Factfile

Favourite book:

....

Favourite CD:

....

Favourite food:

....

Favourite drink:

....

Favourite animal:

....

Favourite pop star:

....

Birthday Wand

1 It was the morning of Aurora's birthday. The Fairies arrived to give her a present.

2 "You can open it later!" said Merryweather, handing Aurora a gift-wrapped box. "There's an even better present for you outside!"

3 Aurora couldn't wait to find out what the other present was. She got dressed and raced outside with Prince Phillip.

50

4 Aurora and Prince Phillip discovered that the Fairies had turned the palace into an amazing pink colour!

5 "It's brilliant!" Aurora told the three fairies. "I'd love to have a pink gown just like it!"

6 "But we've used up all our magic for today!" said Flora, sadly. "There must be something we can do," said Flora.

7 With Aurora and Prince Phillip's help, the three fairies searched their spell books to find more magic to make the pink gown.

8 "Of course!" said Merryweather, at last. "We've used up our daily magic but you haven't, Aurora!"

9 The fairies told Aurora to open her present – it was a magic wand. "Just for today, you are a birthday fairy!" they told her.

10 Aurora waved the wand and made a gown as pink as the palace. And when the Prince asked her to dance, the day was complete!

The End

Use your pens to add some colour to Aurora's ballgown.

Flower Ring

Make and wear this ring to become
a true flower princess!

You will need:

card

scissors

sticky tape

silk rose

glue

purple sequins

1 To make the top of the ring, cut out a circle from card and decorate it with a silk rose and sequins.

2 Next, make a band to fit your finger from card. Finally, glue the band to the top of the ring.

Pretty Necklaces

Aurora is looking at all her pretty necklaces.

Are there more ruby necklaces than pearl necklaces?

Answer:
Yes, there are more ruby necklaces.

Off to the Ball

Who will reach the ball first - Aurora or the Fairy Godmothers? Play this game with a friend to find out!

How to play

First decide who will be Aurora and who will be the Fairy Godmothers. If you are Aurora you need to throw an even number on the dice; 2, 4, 6, to move forward one heart. If you are the Fairy Godmothers you need to throw an odd number on the dice; 1, 3, 5, to move forward a heart. The winner is the first person to reach the palace.

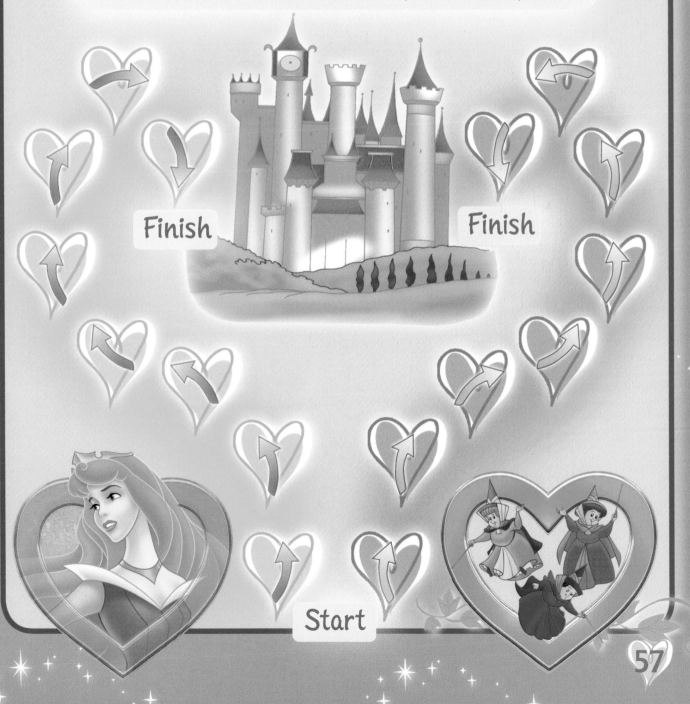

Finish

Finish

Start

Snow White Factfile

Personality:
Kind, caring, sweet
and loving

Romance:
Prince Charming

Appearance:
Shiny, short black hair
and brown eyes

Family:
The Evil Queen

Princess Pet

Complete this fill-in, all about your dream pet.

Draw your dream pet in the space above.

Pet Factfile

Pet's name:

....

Type of animal:

....

Personality:

....

....

Woodland Locket

1 One day, the Prince came to visit Snow White in the forest. "I have a special present for you," he told her.

2 Snow White opened the present and found a locket inside. "It's a woodland locket," the Prince told her. "It has magical powers."

3 Later, Snow White and the Prince were walking through the forest, when a strange magical wind blew past them.

4 The forest grew dark and a wicked enchantress appeared. "I hate the forest and all who live in it!" she cackled and turned the Prince into a cat.

5 "Don't worry, my Prince," said Snow White. "I will break the Enchantress's curse and show her that the forest is full of so many wonderful things."

6 At Snow White's words, her locket began to sparkle, magically. "Of course!" she cried. "It's a woodland locket!"

7 Snow White used the magic of the locket to make the forest full of light and pretty things again.

8 The Enchantress had been changed by the magic, too. "I was wrong," she told Snow White. "The forest really is full of wonderful things."

9 The Enchantress changed the cat back into the Prince. "It was your love for the forest that really saved the day!" the Prince told Snow White.

10 To celebrate, Snow White and the Prince danced with joy. Something that Snow White loved just as much as she loved the forest!

The End

Use the little picture in the wishing well
to help you colour in this page.

Princess Card

Make this Snow White card for a friend.

You will need:

white and pink card, & purple paper

scissors

sequins

pencil

princess picture

glue

yellow material

1 Fold a piece of pink card in half so it opens like a greetings card. Decorate the front with purple paper and sequins.

Note to parents: adult supervision is recommended when sharp-pointed items such as scissors are in use.

2 Trace over this picture of Snow White. Glue yellow material to her skirt and stick blue sequins on to her bodice.

64

3 Make flaps with the white card and glue them on to the front of the card, then glue Snow White on to the flaps so she stands away from the card.

4 Now your card is ready to write a message inside and send to a princess friend!

Tiara Trouble

Oh dear, the jewels have fallen out of Snow White's tiara!

Can you help her decide where they go?

Answers: 1 = b, 2 = d, 3 = a, 4 = e, 5 = f, 6 = g, 7 = c.

Memory Game

How good is your memory? Find out by testing yourself with this Snow White game.

How to play

To test yourself, study this page for two minutes then cover it up with a piece of paper. Write down as many objects as you can remember.

Princess Wordsearch

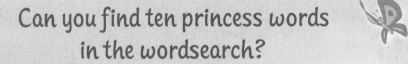

Can you find ten princess words
in the wordsearch?

Look carefully – the words can
be written in any direction.

C	I	N	D	E	R	E	L	L	A
E	C	N	I	R	P	S	G	W	U
T	D	T	Q	I	S	B	P	E	R
I	F	I	L	C	E	N	A	N	O
H	I	A	F	L	T	E	L	I	R
W	A	E	L	E	I	R	A	M	A
W	R	E	B	I	O	P	C	S	I
O	A	J	A	I	O	P	E	A	P
N	I	S	A	A	L	X	F	J	Y
S	T	P	R	I	N	C	E	S	S

PRINCESS
CINDERELLA
ARIEL
BELLE
SNOW
WHITE
AURORA
JASMINE
PRINCE
PALACE
TIARA

Answers:

S	T	P	R	I	N	C	E	S	S
N	I	S	A	A	L	X	F	J	Y
O	A	J	A	I	O	P	E	A	P
W	R	E	B	I	O	P	C	S	I
W	A	E	L	E	I	R	A	M	A
H	I	A	F	L	T	E	L	I	R
I	F	I	L	C	E	N	A	N	O
T	D	T	Q	I	S	B	P	E	R
E	C	N	I	R	P	S	G	W	U
C	I	N	D	E	R	E	L	L	A

Magical moment

Cinderella is arriving at the ball.

Can you add some pretty colours to this enchanting scene?

© Disney

For more magical fun, don't miss Disney's Princess magazine, on sale every two weeks!

Available at all good newsagents and supermarkets.

FREE Jewel bracelet!
Disney's Princess
Every girl can be a Princess!
Things to make • Colouring • Stories